# Dad,
# I Want to Hear
# Your Story

## A Father's
## Guided Journal
## To Share His Life &
## His Love

Jeffrey Mason

**Hear Your Story Books**

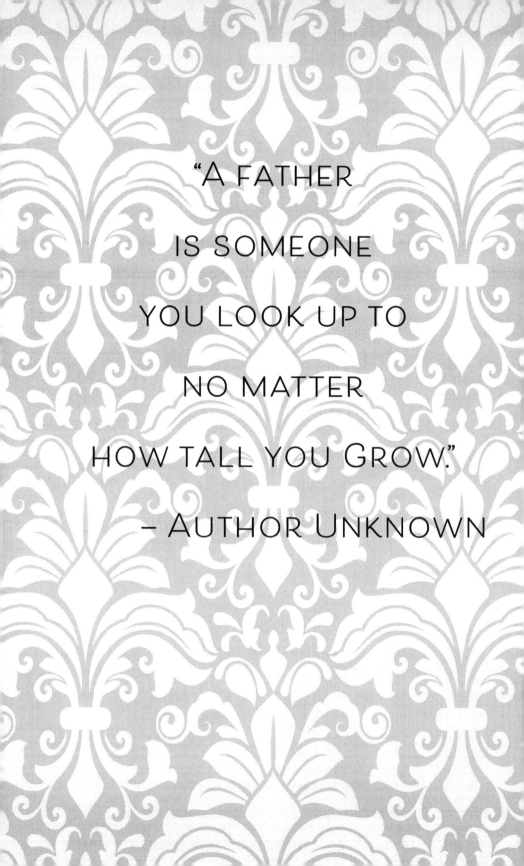

"A FATHER

IS SOMEONE

YOU LOOK UP TO

NO MATTER

HOW TALL YOU GROW."

– AUTHOR UNKNOWN

# THIS BOOK BELONGS TO:

_____

_____

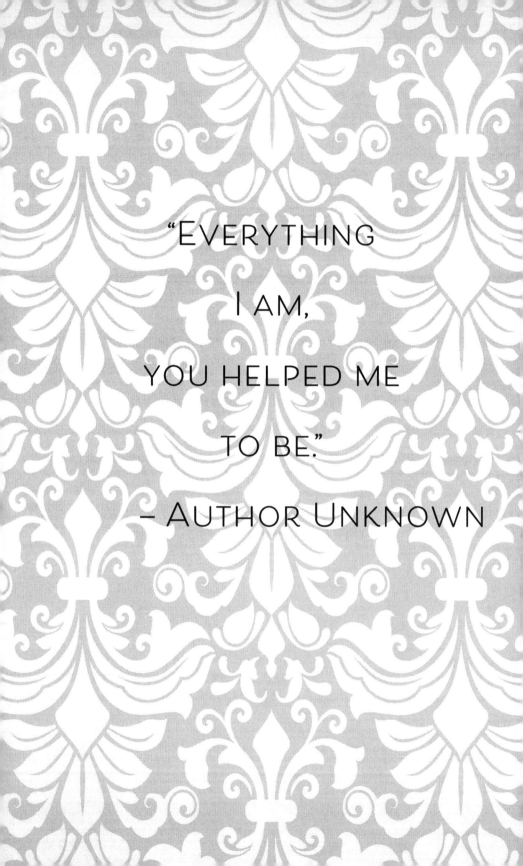

"EVERYTHING
I AM,
YOU HELPED ME
TO BE."
– AUTHOR UNKNOWN

# About This Book

In today's world, time with family too often takes a back seat to the everyday rush and responsibilities. Despite doing our best, we still frequently find ourselves stretched thin, with less and less time to focus on the people in our lives.

The purpose of Dad, I Want to Hear Your Story is to inspire conversations that reconnect us to our families, our pasts and, ultimately, ourselves. Sharing with one another helps to build understanding, empathy, and connection.

When our children know our pasts - where we came from - our hopes and needs, our feelings and fears, they can see us beyond simply what we are to one another, the parent/child dynamic, and can have a more complex and meaningful p picture of us as individuals.

Actively seeking out a deeper understanding of family is what uncovers the treasure that lies in those shared roots: the colorful stories, people, and places that make up the fabric of your family here and now.

My hope is that this book will serve as a pause button on the rush and responsibilities, allowing fathers to talk openly with their children, to be vulnerable, and to learn from one another.

# IT'S YOUR BIRTHDAY!
"Fathering is not something perfect men do,
but something that perfects the man." — Frank Pittman

What is your birthdate?

_____

What was your full name at birth?

_____

Were you named after a relative or someone else of
significance?

_____

_____

_____

In what city were you born?

_____

What was your length and weight at birth?

_____

Were you born in a hospital? If not, where?

_____

_____

What were your first words?

_____

_____

# IT'S YOUR BIRTHDAY!

"Any man can be a father, but it takes
someone special to be a Dad." — Anne Geddes

How old were you when you started to walk?

_____

How old were your parents when you were born?

_____

_____

How did your parents describe you as a baby?

_____

_____

_____

_____

_____

_____

_____

_____

_____

_____

_____

# IT'S YOUR BIRTHDAY!

"The great use of life is to spend it for
something that will outlast it." — William James

What stories have you been told about the day you were
born?

_____

_____

_____

_____

_____

_____

_____

_____

_____

_____

_____

_____

# IT'S YOUR BIRTHDAY!

"There are no perfect parents, but there are many
moments when being a parent is perfect." — Author Unknown

What is a favorite childhood memory?

_____

_____

_____

_____

_____

_____

_____

_____

_____

_____

_____

_____

_____

_____

_____

_____

# WHAT HAPPENED THE YEAR YOU WERE BORN?

"We worry about what a child will become tomorrow,
yet we forget that he is someone today." — Stacia Tauscher

Google the following for the year you were born:
What are some notable events that occurred?

_____

_____

_____

_____

What movie won the Academy Award for Best Picture?
Who won for Best Actor and Best Actress?

_____

_____

_____

What were a few popular movies that came out that year?

_____

_____

_____

_____

# WHAT HAPPENED THE YEAR YOU WERE BORN?

"The most important thing in the
world is family and love." — John Wooden

What song was on the top of the Billboard charts?

_____

Who was the leader of the country (President, Prime Minister, etc.)?

_____

What were a few popular television shows?

_____

_____

_____

_____

_____

What were the prices for the following items?

- A loaf of bread:
- A gallon of milk:
- A cup of coffee:
- A dozen eggs:
- The average cost of a new home:
- A first-class stamp:
- A new car:
- A gallon of gas:
- A movie ticket:

# GROWING UP
"A family needs a father to anchor it."
— L. Tom Perry

How would you describe yourself when you were a kid?

_____

_____

_____

_____

Did you have a nickname when you were growing up? If yes, how did you get it?

_____

Who were your best friends in your elementary school days? Are you still in contact with them?

_____

_____

_____

What were your regular chores? Did you get an allowance? How much was it and what did you spend it on?

_____

_____

_____

# GROWING UP

"My father's love existed through his actions."
— Author Unknown

Describe what your room looked like when you were growing up. Was it messy or clean? Did you have paintings or posters on the walls? What were the main colors?

_____

_____

_____

_____

_____

_____

_____

_____

What is one thing you miss about being a kid?

_____

_____

_____

_____

# DAD TRIVIA

"The best inheritance a parent can give his children is a few minutes of his time each day." — Orlando Aloysius Battista

What is your favorite flavor of ice cream?

_____

How do you like your coffee?

_____

_____

If you could live anywhere in the world for a year with all expenses paid, where would you choose?

_____

_____

_____

How do you like your eggs cooked?

_____

Preference: cook or clean?

_____

What is your shoe size?

_____

What superpower would you choose for yourself?

_____

_____

# DAD TRIVIA

"There can be no keener revelation of a society's soul
than the way in which it treats its children." — Nelson Mandela

Do you have any allergies?

_____

_____

_____

What is your biggest fear?

_____

_____

What would you order as your last meal?

_____

_____

_____

_____

Have you ever broken a bone? Which one(s) and how?

_____

_____

What is your favorite sandwich?

_____

# THE TEENAGE YEARS

"The scariest part of raising a teenager is remembering the things you did when you were a teenager." — Author Unknown

How would you describe yourself when you were a teenager?

_____

_____

_____

_____

_____

How did you dress and style your hair during your teens?

_____

_____

_____

_____

_____

Did you hang out with a group or just a few close friends? Are you still close with any of them?

_____

_____

_____

_____

# THE TEENAGE YEARS

"Teenagehood – that time in life when you show your
individuality by looking like everyone else." — Author Unknown

Describe a typical Friday or Saturday night during your
high school years.

_____

_____

_____

_____

Did you have a curfew?

_____

Did you date during your high school years?

_____

_____

Did you go to any school dances? What were they like?

_____

_____

_____

_____

Who taught you to drive and in what kind of car?

_____

_____

# THE TEENAGE YEARS

"Little children, headache; big children, heartache."
— Italian Proverb

How old were you when you got your first car? What kind of car was it (year, make, and model)?

_____

_____

What school activities or sports did you participate in?

_____

_____

_____

_____

_____

What did you like and dislike about high school?

_____

_____

_____

_____

_____

# THE TEENAGE YEARS

"Keep true to the dreams of your youth."
— Friedrich Schiller

What were your grades like?

_____

_____

Did you have a favorite subject and a least favorite?

_____

_____

_____

What are a few favorite songs from your high school years?

_____

_____

_____

_____

_____

_____

_____

_____

# THE TEENAGE YEARS

"Having a teenager can cause parents to wonder
about each other's heredity." — Author Unknown

Knowing all you know now, what advice would you give to
your teenage self? What might you have done differently in
school if you knew then what you know now?

_____

_____

_____

_____

_____

_____

_____

_____

_____

_____

_____

_____

# THE TEENAGE YEARS

"Life is a winding path through hills and valleys and in
the end, the journey is all that matters." — Author Unknown

Write about a teacher, coach, or other mentor who had a
significant impact on you when you were growing up.

_____

_____

_____

_____

_____

_____

_____

_____

_____

_____

_____

_____

_____

_____

# BEGINNINGS

"We don't stop going to school when we graduate."
— Carol Burnett

What did you do after high school? Did you get a job, serve in the military, go to college or a trade school? Something else?

_____

_____

_____

_____

Why did you make this choice?

_____

_____

_____

_____

_____

If you went to college or trade school, what was your major/the focus of your education?

_____

_____

_____

# BEGINNINGS
"it takes courage to grow up and become who you really are"
— ee cummings

How did this time period impact who you are today?

_____

_____

_____

_____

_____

_____

If you could go back, what, if anything, would you change about this period of your life? Why?

_____

_____

_____

_____

_____

_____

_____

_____

# WORK & CAREER

"Even if you're on the right track, you'll get
run over if you just sit there." — Will Rogers

When you were a kid, what did you want to be when you grew up?

_____

_____

What was your first job? How old were you? How much were you paid?

_____

_____

How many jobs have you had during your lifetime? List a few of your favorites.

_____

_____

_____

_____

What is the least favorite job you have had?

_____

_____

_____

# WORK & CAREER

"I'm a great believer in luck, and I find the
harder I work, the more I have of it." — Thomas Jefferson

Is there a job or profession your parents wanted you to
pursue? What was it?

_____

_____

_____

When people ask you what profession you are/were in, your
response is...

_____

_____

_____

How did you get into this career?

_____

_____

_____

_____

_____

_____

# WORK & CAREER

"Choose a job you love and you will never
have to work a day in your life." — Confucius

What are/were the best parts of this profession?

_____

_____

_____

_____

_____

_____

_____

_____

What aspects did you or do you dislike about it?

_____

_____

_____

_____

_____

# WORK & CAREER

"If people knew how hard I worked to get my mastery,
it wouldn't seem so wonderful after all." — Michelangelo

Who was the best boss you ever had? Why were they such
a good manager?

_____

_____

_____

_____

_____

What are some of your work and career-related
achievements that you are proudest of?

_____

_____

_____

_____

_____

_____

_____

_____

# DAD TRIVIA

"Even though you're growing up, you
should never stop having fun." — Nina Dobrev

Have you ever been told that you look like someone famous?
If yes, who?

_____

_____

_____

What is your morning routine?

_____

_____

_____

_____

What is a favorite guilty pleasure?

_____

_____

_____

Which television family most reminds you of your family?

_____

_____

# DAD TRIVIA

"It is easier for a father to have children than for
children to have a real father." — Pope John XXIII

Did you have braces? If yes, how old were you when you
got them?

_____

Do you like roller coasters?

_____

_____

What name would you choose if you had to change your
first name?

_____

Did you ever skip school?

_____

If yes, did you get away with it and what did you do during
the time you should have been in class?

_____

_____

_____

_____

_____

_____

# FAMILY TREE
"Each of us is tomorrow's ancestors."
— Author Unknown

My Great-Grandmother
(My Grandmother's Mom)

My Great-Grandmother
(My Grandfather's Mom)

My Great-Grandfather
(My Grandmother's Dad)

My Great-Grandfather
(My Grandfather's Dad)

My Grandmother
(My Mom's Mom)

My Grandfather
(My Mom's Dad)

My Mother

# FAMILY TREE

"As you do for your ancestors, your children will do for you."
— African Proverb

_____
My Great-Grandmother
(My Grandmother's Mom)

_____
My Great-Grandmother
(My Grandfather's Mom)

_____
My Great-Grandfather
(My Grandmother's Dad)

_____
My Great-Grandfather
(My Grandfather's Dad)

_____
My Grandmother
(My Dad's Mom)

_____
My Grandfather
(My Dad's Dad)

_____
My Father

# PARENTS & GRANDPARENTS

"If evolution really works, how come
mothers only have two hands?" — Milton Berle

Where was your mother born and where did she grow up?

_____

_____

_____

What three words would you use to describe her?

_____

_____

_____

In what ways are you most like your mother?

_____

_____

_____

_____

_____

_____

_____

# PARENTS & GRANDPARENTS
"You will never look back on life and think,
'I spent too much time with my kids.'" — Author Unknown

Where was your father born and where did he grow up?

_____

_____

_____

What three words would you use to describe him?

_____

_____

_____

In what ways are you most like your father?

_____

_____

_____

_____

_____

_____

_____

# PARENTS & GRANDPARENTS

"A moment lasts for seconds but the memory of it lasts forever."
— Author Unknown

What is a favorite memory of your mother?

_____

_____

_____

_____

_____

_____

_____

_____

_____

_____

_____

_____

_____

_____

# PARENTS & GRANDPARENTS
"We don't remember days, we remember moments."
— Author Unknown

What is a favorite memory of your father?

_____

_____

_____

_____

_____

_____

_____

_____

_____

_____

_____

_____

_____

# PARENTS & GRANDPARENTS

"To forget one's ancestors is to be a brook without
a source, a tree without a root." — Chinese Proverb

What was your mother's maiden name?

_____

Do you know from what part(s) of the world your mother's
family originates?

_____

_____

_____

Do you know your father's mother's maiden name?

_____

_____

Do you know from what part(s) of the world your father's
family originates?

_____

_____

_____

How did your parents meet?

_____

_____

_____

# PARENTS & GRANDPARENTS

"Appreciate your parents. You never know what
sacrifices they went through for you." — Author Unknown

How would you describe their relationship?

_____

_____

_____

_____

_____

What were your parents' occupations?

_____

_____

_____

Did either of them have any unique talents or skills?

_____

_____

_____

_____

Did either of them serve in the military?

_____

# PARENTS & GRANDPARENTS

"Love is the chain whereby to bind a child to its parents."
— Abraham Lincoln

What is a favorite family tradition that was passed down from your parents or grandparents?

_____

_____

_____

What are a few of your favorite things that your mother or father would cook for the family?

_____

_____

_____

What were your grandparents like on your mother's side?

_____

_____

_____

_____

_____

# PARENTS & GRANDPARENTS

"Next to God, thy parents."
— William Penn

Do you know where your mother's parents were born and grew up?

_____

_____

_____

_____

What were your grandparents like on your father's side?

_____

_____

_____

_____

_____

Do you know where your father's parents were born and grew up?

_____

_____

_____

# PARENTS & GRANDPARENTS

"There is no school equal to a decent home and no
teacher equal to a virtuous parent." — Mahatma Gandhi

What is some of the best advice your mother gave you?

_____

_____

_____

_____

_____

_____

_____

_____

_____

_____

_____

_____

_____

_____

# PARENTS & GRANDPARENTS

"The father who does not teach his son his duties is
equally guilty with the son who neglects them." — Confucius

What is some of the best advice your father gave you?

_____

_____

_____

_____

_____

_____

_____

_____

_____

_____

_____

_____

_____

_____

_____

# PARENTS & GRANDPARENTS

"My fathers planted for me, and I planted for my children."
— Hebrew Saying

Did you ever meet your great-grandparents on either side of your family? If yes, what were they like?

_____

_____

_____

_____

_____

_____

_____

_____

_____

_____

_____

_____

_____

_____

# PARENTS & GRANDPARENTS
"The longest road out is the shortest road home."
— Irish Proverb

What other individuals had a major role in helping you grow up?

_____

_____

_____

_____

_____

_____

_____

_____

_____

_____

_____

_____

_____

_____

# YOUR SIBLINGS
"Brothers and sisters are as close as hands and feet."
— Vietnamese Saying

Are you an only child, or do you have siblings?

_____

Are you the oldest, middle, or youngest?

_____

List your siblings' names in order of their ages. Make sure to include yourself.

_____

_____

_____

_____

_____

Which of your siblings were you the closest with growing up?

_____

_____

Which of your siblings are you the closest with in your adult years?

_____

_____

# YOUR SIBLINGS
"The greatest gift our parents ever gave us was each other."
— Author Unknown

How would you describe each of your siblings when they were kids?

_____

_____

_____

_____

_____

_____

How would you describe each of your siblings as adults?

_____

_____

_____

_____

_____

_____

_____

_____

# YOUR SIBLINGS
"First a brother, then a bother, now a friend."
— Author Unknown

In the following pages, share some favorite memories of each of your siblings. If you're an only child, feel free to share memories of close friends or cousins.

_____

_____

_____

_____

_____

_____

_____

_____

_____

_____

_____

_____

# YOUR SIBLINGS

"What causes sibling rivalry? Having more than one kid."
— Tim Allen

Memories...

_____

_____

_____

_____

_____

_____

_____

_____

_____

_____

_____

_____

_____

_____

_____

_____

# YOUR SIBLINGS

"Siblings know how to push each other's buttons, but they also know how to mend things faster than anyone." — Author Unknown

Memories...

_____

_____

_____

_____

_____

_____

_____

_____

_____

_____

_____

_____

_____

_____

# YOUR SIBLINGS

"The advantage of growing up with siblings is that
you become very good at fractions." — Author Unknown

Memories...

_____

_____

_____

_____

_____

_____

_____

_____

_____

_____

_____

_____

_____

_____

_____

_____

# BECOMING & BEING A DAD

"What can you do to promote world peace?
Go home and love your family." — Mother Teresa

How old were you when you first wanted to become a father?

_____

How old were you when you did become a father?

_____

Who was the first person you told you were going to be a dad?

_____

_____

_____

Describe their reaction.

_____

_____

_____

_____

_____

_____

_____

# BECOMING & BEING A DAD

"Of all the titles I have been privileged to have,
'Dad' has always been the best." — Ken Norton

What were your children's lengths and weights at birth?

_____

_____

_____

_____

_____

Were your kids' deliveries early, late, or on-time?

_____

_____

_____

Is there a special song or songs you would sing or play to
your children when they were little?

_____

_____

_____

_____

# BECOMING & BEING A DAD

"Every father should remember that one day his child
will follow his example, not his advice." — Charles Kettering

Looking back, what would you change about how your kids
were brought up, if anything?

_____

_____

_____

_____

_____

_____

_____

_____

_____

_____

_____

_____

_____

# BECOMING & BEING A DAD

"Before I got married, I had six theories about raising children;
now, I have six children and no theories." — John Wilmot

What are the biggest differences in how kids are raised
today and when you were young?

_____

_____

_____

_____

_____

_____

_____

_____

_____

_____

_____

_____

_____

_____

# BECOMING & BEING A DAD

"By the time a man realizes that maybe his father was right, he usually has a son who thinks he's wrong." — Charles Wadsworth

What are the best and hardest parts of being a father?

_____

_____

_____

_____

_____

_____

_____

_____

_____

_____

_____

_____

_____

_____

# BECOMING & BEING A DAD

"A father's goodness is higher than the mountain,
a mother's goodness deeper than the sea." — Japanese Proverb

Write about a favorite memory of being a father.

_____

_____

_____

_____

_____

_____

_____

_____

_____

_____

_____

_____

_____

_____

# BECOMING & BEING A DAD

"Pretty much all the honest truth telling there is in
the world is done by children." — Oliver Wendell Holmes

Knowing what you know now, what advice would you give
yourself as a new father?

_____

_____

_____

_____

_____

_____

_____

_____

_____

_____

_____

_____

_____

# BECOMING & BEING A DAD

"My father didn't tell me how to live. He lived and
let me watch him do it." — Clarence Budington Kelland

Based upon all you have learned and experienced, what
advice would you give your children?

_____

_____

_____

_____

_____

_____

_____

_____

_____

_____

_____

_____

_____

_____

# LET'S TALK ABOUT YOUR KIDS

"It is easier to build strong children than
to repair broken men." — Frederick Douglass

What would your kids have been named if they were born the opposite gender?

_____

_____

_____

_____

Who did they most look like when they were babies?

_____

_____

_____

_____

What were their first words?

_____

_____

_____

_____

_____

# LET'S TALK ABOUT YOUR KIDS

"Blessed indeed is the man who hears many
gentle voices call him father." — Lydia Maria Child

How old were they when they took their first steps?

_____

_____

_____

Were any of your children "surprises?"

_____

_____

_____

Are there any specific books you remember reading to your kids?

_____

_____

When your kids were little, what trick did you use to calm them when they were upset?

_____

_____

_____

_____

# LET'S TALK ABOUT YOUR KIDS

"Adults are just outdated children."
— Dr. Seuss

In what ways are your kids like you?

_____

_____

_____

_____

_____

_____

_____

_____

_____

_____

_____

_____

_____

_____

_____

_____

# LET'S TALK ABOUT YOUR KIDS
"The sun at home warms better than the sun elsewhere."
— Albanian Proverb

How are they different?

_____

_____

_____

_____

_____

_____

_____

_____

_____

_____

_____

_____

_____

_____

# DAD TRIVIA

"A father is a man who expects his children
to be as good as he meant to be." — Carol Coats

If you could do any one thing for a day, what would it be?

_____

_____

What is your favorite season? What are some things you
love about that time of the year?

_____

_____

_____

What is a smell that reminds you of your childhood? Why?

_____

_____

_____

What is your least favorite household chore?

_____

_____

What do you do better than anyone else in the family?

_____

_____

_____

# DAD TRIVIA

"A father is someone you look up to no
matter how tall you grow." — Author Unknown

What is your favorite dessert?

_____

What is a favorite memory from the last twelve months?

_____

_____

_____

If you could only eat three things for the next year (with
no effect on your health), what would you pick?

_____

_____

_____

What is your definition of success?

_____

_____

_____

_____

_____

# SPIRITUALITY & RELIGION

"We are not human beings having a spiritual experience; we are
spiritual beings having a human experience."
— Pierre Teilhard de Chardin

What do you believe is the purpose of life?

_____

_____

_____

_____

_____

_____

_____

Which has the most impact on our lives: fate or free will?

_____

_____

_____

_____

_____

# SPIRITUALITY & RELIGION

"I believe that what we become depends on what our fathers
teach us at odd moments, when they aren't trying to teach us."
— Umberto Eco, *Foucault's Pendulam*

Were your parents religious when you were growing up?
How did they express their spiritual beliefs?

_____

_____

_____

_____

_____

_____

_____

_____

_____

_____

_____

_____

_____

_____

# SPIRITUALITY & RELIGION

"Within you there is a stillness and a sanctuary to which you
can retreat at any time and be yourself." — Hermann Hesse

How have your spiritual or religious beliefs and practices
changed over the course of your life?

_____

_____

_____

_____

_____

_____

_____

_____

_____

_____

_____

_____

_____

# SPIRITUALITY & RELIGION

"What you are is God's gift to you, what you become
is your gift to God." — Hans Urs von Balthasar, *Prayer*

What religious or spiritual practices do you incorporate
into your daily life today, if any?

_____

_____

_____

_____

_____

_____

Do you believe in miracles? Have you experienced one?

_____

_____

_____

_____

_____

_____

# SPIRITUALITY & RELIGION

"When you arise in the morning think of what a privilege it is to
be alive, to think, to enjoy, to love." — Marcus Aurelius

What do you do when times are challenging, and you need
to find additional inner strength?

_____

_____

_____

_____

_____

_____

_____

_____

_____

_____

_____

_____

# SPIRITUALITY & RELIGION

"Families are like branches on a tree. We grow in different
directions, yet our roots remain as one." — Author Unknown

Write about a time you found relief by forgiving someone.

_____

_____

_____

_____

_____

_____

_____

_____

_____

_____

_____

_____

_____

_____

_____

_____

# LOVE & ROMANCE

"We are asleep until we fall in love!"
— Leo Tolstoy, *War and Peace*

Do you believe in love at first sight?

_____

_____

_____

Do you believe in soulmates?

_____

_____

_____

How old were you when you had your first kiss?

_____

What age were you when you went on your first date?

_____

Can you remember who it was with and what you did?

_____

_____

_____

_____

_____

# LOVE & ROMANCE

*"Whatever our souls are made of, his and mine are the same."*
— Emily Brontë, *Wuthering Heights*

How old were you when you had your first steady relationship? Who was it with?

_____

How many times in your life have you been in love?

_____

_____

What are some of the most important qualities of a successful relationship?

_____

_____

_____

_____

_____

_____

_____

_____

_____

_____

# LOVE & ROMANCE

"We loved with a love that was more than love."
— Edgar Allan Poe, *Annabel Lee*

Did you have any celebrity crushes when you were young?

_____

_____

_____

Were you ever in a relationship with someone your parents did not approve of?

_____

_____

_____

Have you ever written someone or had someone write you a love poem or song?

_____

If yes, write a few lines that you may remember.

_____

_____

_____

_____

_____

_____

# LOVE & ROMANCE

"Love is a great beautifier."
— Louisa May Alcott, *Little Women*

In what ways do you feel your parents' relationship
influenced how you have approached love and marriage?

_____

_____

_____

_____

_____

_____

Write about a favorite romantic moment.

_____

_____

_____

_____

_____

_____

_____

# LOVE & ROMANCE
"We don't remember days, we remember moments."
— Author Unknown

How did you meet our Mom?

_____

_____

_____

_____

What was your first impression of her?

_____

_____

_____

_____

_____

What is your proposal story?

_____

_____

_____

_____

# LOVE & ROMANCE

"Children are the hands by which we take hold of heaven."
— Henry Ward Beecher

What was your wedding like? Where was it held and who was there? Any good wedding day stories?

_____

_____

_____

_____

_____

_____

_____

_____

_____

_____

_____

_____

_____

# TRAVEL

"Once a year, go someplace you've never been before."
— Dali Lama

Do you have a valid passport?

_____

How do you feel about cruises?

_____

_____

How do you feel about flying?

_____

What are a few of your favorite places that you've traveled to?

_____

_____

_____

_____

_____

_____

_____

_____

# TRAVEL
"Life is short, and the world is wide."
— Author Unknown

What is a favorite travel memory?

_____

_____

_____

_____

_____

_____

_____

_____

_____

_____

_____

_____

_____

# TRAVEL BUCKET LIST

"Man cannot discover new oceans unless he has
the courage to lose sight of the shore." — André Gide

List the top 10 places you would visit if money and time
were no concern.

1. _____

_____

2. _____

_____

3. _____

_____

4. _____

_____

5. _____

_____

# TRAVEL BUCKET LIST

"The world is a book, and those who do not
travel read only one page." — Saint Augustine

6. _____

_____

7. _____

_____

8. _____

_____

9. _____

_____

10. _____

_____

# DAD TRIVIA

"Anyone who does anything to help a child in his life is a hero."
— Fred Rogers

What would you title your autobiography?

_____

_____

_____

Do you think you could still pass the written portion of
the driver's test without studying?

_____

What is your favorite color?

_____

What is your favorite quote?

_____

_____

_____

Do you believe in life on other planets?

_____

If you could travel through time and had to choose, who
would you meet: your ancestors or your descendants?

_____

_____

# DAD TRIVIA
"Noble fathers have noble children."
— Euripides

What personal accomplishments are you most proud of?

_____

_____

_____

_____

_____

What are five things you are grateful for?

_____

_____

_____

_____

If you were forced to sing karaoke, what song would you perform?

_____

_____

_____

# POLITICAL STUFF

"What you teach your children, you also teach their children."
— Author Unknown

Which best describes how you feel about having political discussions:

- ☐ I would rather not.
- ☐ I prefer to have them with people whose views match mine.
- ☐ I love a good debate.

How old were you the first time you voted?

_____

What are the biggest differences in your political views today and when you were in your early twenties?

_____

_____

_____

_____

Have you ever taken part in a march or boycott? What issues, if any, could motivate you to join one?

_____

_____

_____

_____

# POLITICAL STUFF

"In politics stupidity is not a handicap."
— Napoleon Bonaparte

When was the last time you voted?

_____

In what ways do you agree and disagree with the political
choices of your children's generation?

_____

_____

_____

_____

_____

_____

If you woke up to find yourself in charge of the country,
what are the first three things you would enact or change?

One: _____

_____

Two: _____

_____

Three: _____

_____

# SPORTS MEMORIES

"Anyone can be a father, but it takes
someone special to be a dad." — Wade Boggs

When you were a kid, did you ever think about being a professional athlete? Which sports?

_____

_____

Growing up, what was your favorite sport? Did you have a favorite team?

_____

_____

_____

_____

Who is your favorite player of all time in any sport?

_____

_____

_____

If money was no object, what sporting event would you most want to attend?

_____

_____

_____

# SPORTS MEMORIES

"My father gave me the greatest gift anyone could
give another person; he believed in me." — Jim Valvano

What was the first professional sporting event you attended
in person?

_____

_____

_____

What was the most crushing defeat you experienced playing
or watching a sporting event?

_____

_____

_____

Is there a sporting event you saw as a kid that you still
vividly remember?

_____

_____

_____

What is your favorite sports movie?

_____

_____

_____

# MOVIES, MUSIC, TELEVISION, & BOOKS

"If you want a happy ending, that depends, of course, on where you stop your story." — Orson Welles

What movie have you watched the greatest number of times?

_____

_____

What movie or television show can you remember loving when you were a kid?

_____

_____

Who would you cast to play yourself in the movie of your life? How about for the rest of your family?

_____

_____

_____

_____

_____

_____

_____

_____

# MOVIES, MUSIC, TELEVISION, & BOOKS

"Children are the living messages we send
to a time we will not see." — John F. Kennedy

What are your favorite genres of music?

_____

_____

_____

_____

Which decades had the best music?

_____

_____

_____

_____

What is the first record (or cassette, cd, etc.) you can
remember buying or being given as a gift?

_____

_____

What song do you like today that would make your younger
self cringe?

_____

_____

# MOVIES, MUSIC, TELEVISION, & BOOKS

"When I was a kid, my parents moved a lot,
but I always found them." — Rodney Dangerfield

What is a song from your teens that reminds you of a special event or moment?

_____

_____

_____

What song would you pick as the theme song of your life?

_____

_____

_____

What was the first concert you attended? Where was it held and when?

_____

_____

How has your taste in music changed over the years?

_____

_____

_____

_____

# MOVIES, MUSIC, TELEVISION, & BOOKS

"The greatest gifts you can give your children are the roots of responsibility and the wings of independence." — Denis Waitley

What television show from the past do you wish was still on the air?

_____

If you could be cast in any television show or movie, past or present, which one would you choose?

_____

What are some favorite books from your childhood and/or teenage years?

_____

_____

_____

What book or books have majorly impacted the way you think, work, or live your life?

_____

_____

_____

_____

_____

# TOP TEN MOVIES

"Children need models rather than critics."
— Joseph Joubert

List up to ten of your most favorite movies:

1. _____

2. _____

3. _____

4. _____

5. _____

6. _____

7. _____

8. _____

9. _____

10. _____

# TOP TEN SONGS
"The music is not in the notes, but in the silence in between."
— Wolfgang Amadeus Mozart

List up to ten of your most favorite songs:

1. _____

2. _____

3. _____

4. _____

5. _____

6. _____

7. _____

8. _____

9. _____

10. _____

# DAD TRIVIA
"Once a father, forever a father."
— Author Unknown

What is your favorite holiday and why?

_____

_____

_____

_____

Is there anything in your family's medical history that your kids should know about?

_____

_____

_____

_____

Which ten-year period of your life has been your favorite so far and why?

_____

_____

_____

_____

# DAD TRIVIA

"Let me love you a little more before you're not little anymore."
— Author Unknown

Who would you invite if you could have dinner with any five people who have ever lived?

_____

_____

_____

_____

_____

What are some of your most favorite books?

_____

_____

_____

_____

_____

_____

_____

_____

# ROOM FOR MORE

"Children are everything adults wish they could be."
— Author Unknown

The following pages are for you to expand on some of your answers, to share more memories, and/or to write notes to your loved ones:

_____

_____

_____

_____

_____

_____

_____

_____

_____

_____

_____

_____

_____

# ROOM FOR MORE

"Children are apt to live up to what you believe of them."
— Lady Bird Johnson

---

# ROOM FOR MORE

"When you have brought up kids, there are memories
you store directly in your tear ducts." — Robert Brault

_____

_____

_____

_____

_____

_____

_____

_____

_____

_____

_____

_____

_____

_____

# ROOM FOR MORE

"Children are like wet cement: whatever
falls on them makes an impression." — Haim Ginott

---

---

---

---

---

---

---

---

---

---

---

---

---

---

# ROOM FOR MORE

"A father is the one friend upon whom we can always rely."
— Emile Gaboriau

# ROOM FOR MORE

"It's the most profound gift and the most daunting challenge."
— Matt Bomer

_____

_____

_____

_____

_____

_____

_____

_____

_____

_____

_____

_____

_____

# ROOM FOR MORE

"A dad wants to catch you when you fall, but instead picks
you up, brushes you off and lets you try again." — Author Unknown

_____

_____

_____

_____

_____

_____

_____

_____

_____

_____

_____

_____

_____

_____

# ROOM FOR MORE

"Dad, your guiding hand on my shoulder will
remain with me forever." — Author Unknown

_____

_____

_____

_____

_____

_____

_____

_____

_____

_____

_____

_____

_____

# HEAR YOUR STORY BOOKS

At **Hear Your Story**, we have created a line of books focused on giving each of us a place to tell the unique story of who we are, where we have been, and where we are going.

Sharing and hearing the stories of the people in our lives creates a closeness and understanding, ultimately strengthening our bonds.

## Available at Amazon, all bookstores, and HearYourStoryBooks.com

- Mom, I Want to Hear Your Story: A Mother's Guided Journal to Share Her Life & Her Love

- Dad, I Want to Hear Your Story: A Father's Guided Journal to Share His Life & His Love

- Grandfather, I Want to Hear Your Story: A Grandfather's Guided Journal to Share His Life and His Love

- Tell Your Life Story: The Write Your Own Autobiography Guided Journal

- Life Gave Me You; I Want to Hear Your Story: A Guided Journal for Stepmothers to Share Their Life Story

- You Choose to Be My Dad; I Want to Hear Your Story: A Guided Journal for Stepdads to Share Their Life Story

# HEAR YOUR STORY BOOKS

- To My Wonderful Aunt, I Want to Hear Your Story: A Guided Journal to Share Her Life and Her Love

- To My Uncle, I Want to Hear Your Story: A Guided Journal to Share His Life and His Love

- Mom, I Want to Learn Your Recipes: A Keepsake Memory Book to Gather and Preserve Your Favorite Family Recipes

- Dad, I Want to Learn Your Recipes: A Keepsake Memory Book to Gather and Preserve Your Favorite Family Recipes

- Grandmother, I Want to Learn Your Recipes: A Keepsake Memory Book to Gather and Preserve Your Favorite Family Recipes

- Grandfather, I Want to Learn Your Recipes: A Keepsake Memory Book to Gather and Preserve Your Favorite Family Recipes

- Aunt, I Want to Learn Your Recipes: A Keepsake Memory Book to Gather and Preserve Your Favorite Family Recipes

- Uncle, I Want to Learn Your Recipes: A Keepsake Memory Book to Gather and Preserve Your Favorite Family Recipes

- To My Girlfriend, I Want to Hear Your Story

- To My Boyfriend, I Want to Hear Your Story

- Mom & Me: Let's Learn Together Journal for Kids

# DEDICATION

To Tommie Louis Mason
My Dad

You were my first example, my forever mentor.

We are alike in temperament
and the same in spirit.
The lesson of your life was
to live and love with all I am,
to never give up and to always find a way.

Most important of all,
you taught me to love who I am
and always believe that I deserve *amazing*.

Thank you for your love, your example, and your
passion for the discovery of what is possible.

I Love You Dad.

Dear goodness, I miss you.

# ABOUT THE AUTHOR

Jeffrey Mason is the creator and author of the best-selling **Hear Your Story®** line of books and is the founder of the company **Hear Your Story®**.

In response to his own father's fight with Alzheimer's, Jeffrey wrote his first two books, **Mom, I Want to Hear Your Story** and **Dad, I Want to Hear Your Story** in 2019. Since then, he has written and designed over 30 books, been published in four languages, and sold over 300,000 copies worldwide.

Jeffrey is dedicated to spreading the mission that the little things are the big things and that each of us has an incredible life story that needs to be shared and celebrated. He continues to create books that he hopes will guide people to reflect on and share their full life experience, while creating opportunities for talking, listening, learning, and understanding.

**Hear Your Story®** can be visited at **hearyourstorybooks.com** and Jeffrey can be contacted for questions, comments, podcasting, speaking engagements, or just a hello at **jeffrey.mason@hearyourstory.com**.

He would be grateful if you would help people find his books by leaving a review on Amazon. Your feedback helps him get better at this thing he loves.

# VIEW THIS BOOK
# ON YOUR COMPUTER

We invite you to also check out HearYourStory.com, where you can answer the questions in this book using your smart phone, tablet, or computer.

Answering the questions online at HearYourStory.com allows you to write as much as you want, to save your responses and revisit and revise them whenever you wish, and to print as many copies as you need for you and your whole family.

Please note there is a small one-time charge to cover the cost of maintaining the site.

ISBN: 978-1-955034-74-6

Made in the USA
Columbia, SC
04 June 2024

e56c1417-b1be-4103-9137-24edf36d140cR01